PARENTIN

By the time we get the hang of p: .!
Most of us have had to learn pa   -
knocks. But isn't it wiser to lear.. .... uns
course—it will amuse, motivate, inspire and equip. We wish we'd been
able to take this course before we started parenting our teenagers!

Killy and J John

An ever-increasing number of families and churches are desperate to
find a resource to equip parents in the challenge and privilege of bringing up teens. We piloted this course, and it has made a huge impact and
has been so well received—an excellent resource, straightforward, enjoy-
able, balanced and biblical, from those who have themselves a proven
and practical track record in bringing up their own teenagers. We highly
recommend this course to you and your church.

Mark and Karen Bailey

We at New Wine have always valued our young people and so we are
thrilled that Paul and Christine have provided, at our invitation, a 'Family Time' sequel. Every church wanting to help teenagers and their parents needs to have this resource among its family life courses.

John and Anne Coles

This handbook is intended to be used in conjunction with the six-session Family Time course *Parenting Teenagers*, as a sequel to the *Parenting Children* Course. A handbook should be provided for each participant on the course.

It contains:

- A course outline
- An Introduction to each session
- Main points from the speaker's notes
- Individual and group exercises
- Discussion Group scenarios and questions
- Taking it Further exercises
- Suggested reading

Bible references are taken from the New International Version.

More information on courses, delegate materials, downloadable speakers' resources, invitations and posters is available via the Family Time website www.family-time.co.uk, or phone Family Time on 020 8799 3778.

Parenting Teenagers

Course Handbook

PAUL AND CHRISTINE PERKIN

KINGSWAY PUBLICATIONS
EASTBOURNE

Cover design by Pinnacle Creative (www.pinnaclecreative.co.uk)

ISBN 978–1–842913–66–6

Published by
KINGSWAY COMMUNICATIONS LTD
Lottbridge Drove, Eastbourne BN23 6NT, England.
Email: books@kingsway.co.uk

Printed in Great Britain

Course Outline

Session 1
A GALAXY FAR, FAR AWAY
The Teenage Universe

INTRODUCTION TO THE SESSION

- We'll be taking an overview of the teenage years, the different worlds that we and they are now living in; asking questions about ourselves as much as about our teenagers.
- We'll look at some of the changes that have arisen and are continuing to evolve, the issues that arise in this period, and some strategies for negotiating these changes.
- We'll be looking not so much for problems and differences as growth points in understanding; to overcome barriers, build bridges and reduce spaces between us.

A. PARALLEL UNIVERSES

Understanding our world

Exercise:
Can you answer the following questions about yourself?
1. *What sort of personality do you have?*
   (easy-going, ambitious, perfectionist, pessimistic. . .)

2. *What sort of home do you think you run?*
   (permissive, strict, easy-going. . .)

3. *What particularly pressurises you?*
   (work, money, health, relationships. . .)

4. *What is important to you in life?*
   (education, sport, lifestyle, religious faith. . .)

5. *What or who most influences you?*
   (peer group, spouse, your own parents. . .)

Flashback

Exercise:
Try to remember when you were 14 or 15 years old:

1. Whose opinion mattered most in all the world to you?

2. Can you name three friends whose homes you liked going to? Why did you like these in particular?

3. Do you remember the first boy/girl you were attracted to?

4. What annoyed you most about your parents? Can you remember specific things they said or did that embarrassed you?

5. What 'idols' did you have through your teenage years? Was there a pop group, film star or football team that you were besotted with?

6. Can you name three things that were sacrosanct in your family when you were a teenager? E.g. meals must be eaten in the kitchen or dining room, not in front of the TV.

7. *Was there someone you fancied who hardly seemed to even notice you? What did it feel like?*

8. *Can you remember your parents denying you something? How did you react?*

Understanding their world

1. Their likes

Exercise:
Can you answer the following questions about one of your teenagers?

(a) What are the names of their three best friends?

(b) What are their favourite TV programmes?

(c) What kind of music do they listen to – do you know the names of the artists?

(d) What is their latest fashion 'essential'?

(e) Where do they spend their evenings out – what do they do?

(f) Who influences their opinions most?

(g) What do they find difficult in their relationship with you?

(h) Do you know how they most recently spent more than £20?

The following is adapted from material by Nicky and Sila Lee.

2. Their needs

What kind of home are we trying to create for our family through these teenage years?

(a) **A place to be known**
   – where they will be loved unconditionally
   – where they can be open and honest
   – where they can make mistakes and move on

(b)   A place to grow
- where they will grow in confidence
- where their opinions are valued
- where they can face disappointment

(c)   A place to laugh
- where there is teasing and easy banter
- where there are family traditions
- where their friends will be welcome

(d)   A place to retreat
- where they will feel safe
- where they will find support from outside pressures
- where they will be heard and understood

Bible View:

'How great is the love the Father has lavished on us, that we should be called children of God! And that is what we are!' (1 John 3:1)

The basis of a secure, growing, light-hearted and accepting home is to know our home within God's family. We don't have to try to be God's children. By faith in him we are already members of his family, which means that nothing we can ever do will make him love us more and nothing we can ever do will make him love us less.

Exercise:
In pairs, ask each other the question: What kind of home are we creating?

- *Which of the four above are our strengths?*

• *Which of the four are weaknesses?*

B. BLACK HOLES THAT EAT UP TIME

Understanding their greatest need

1. Being available

'They need you as a base they can return to, a sheltered harbour, so that when the storm gets rough they can head back to you.' (Paul Francis)

> Bible View:
>
> 'I have no-one else like him, who takes a genuine interest in your welfare.'(Philippians 2:20)
>
> Paul's estimate of his close friend Timothy is a model for all parents – a genuine interest in and concern for the welfare of those closest to us. Love has been defined as 'unconditional responsibility for and unconditional availability to others, physically, mentally, materially, emotionally and spiritually'. The starting point of that kind of love involves spending time and energy.

Exercise:
How available do we feel we are to our teenagers?

What makes us less available through these years?

• *Are there younger siblings to look after?*
• *Are new career opportunities opening up?*

- *Are there other emotional pressures on you?*
- *Are sporting or social activities taking up time?*

2. Being honest

'Quality time' versus 'quantity time':

> 'Quality time is a myth created by adults. The concept of quality time is driven by the need of the parents, who are often over-committed and try to assign a few minutes of their hectic schedules to activities devoted to their children and call it quality time.' (Tim Smith in *Almost Cool*)

One parent's observation: 'There's an awful lot of just "hanging around" where teenagers are concerned!'

3. Being imaginative

Think what they would like to do – not what you would like to do with them!

Exercise:
Think of some particularly good memories of things you've done together – either individually or as a family:

- *What made them special?*
- *How could you recreate them without trying to turn back the clock?*

Turn and share with the person next to you.

C. A QUESTION OF RELATIVITY

Understanding change

> 'Parents face two options. We can keep using the same patterns we used when they were young (and frustrate ourselves to death), or we can come to realise

that our methods must change as our kids develop. . .' (Daniel Hahn – youth pastor)

The four 'R's to help us move with change:

RECOGNISE – when we have reached a time of change.

RELAX – be gentle with ourselves and with them.

REJOICE – enjoy who our children are.

RELEASE – them.

Bible View:

'Don't be afraid; just believe, and she will be healed.'(Luke 8:50)

The words of reassurance Jesus gave to one father, Jairus, about his daughter, in the face of crisis – a promise to cling on to in times of climactic change.

Exercise:
In pairs, ask the questions:

• *How well do you feel you are working out the four 'R's as your family changes around you?*
• *Is there one you could do something about right now?*

DISCUSSION GROUPS

Scenarios

1. We used to be a wonderfully close family and always did fun things together at the weekends. But suddenly our 15-year-old son refuses to take part in any family activities. He either stays in his room with the door shut listening to music, or he goes out on his bike to meet his mates. I'm afraid that his siblings will simply follow his lead and we'll have no family time left at all. What should we do?

2. We have always spent family summer holidays together in a cottage in Devon. Our 18-year-old daughter has suddenly announced that she has made alternative plans to go with some friends to Spain. Our 16-year-old is now up in arms and says that if her sister isn't coming with us, she doesn't want to come either. What should we still expect? When do you allow them to make plans of their own?

3. I have three teenagers of 13, 14 and 16. I have just taken on a job that means I won't be home until 6 pm most evenings. I've always been there for them when they've come in from school, and I'm unsure whether this is a right move to make at this stage in their teens. What would you advise?

Follow-up questions

1. How do you hold together the 'top end' of your family with the younger members? How is your time divided between your different children?

2. Do you have particular shared activities with your teenagers? How do you see these changing/developing as they get older? What new activities could you instigate?

TAKING IT FURTHER

Review of the year

For each child, ask yourself:

- How has the last year been for them and for my relationship with them?
- What have been some of the frustrations in my relationship with my teenager? How could we tackle them?
- What are some of the things we enjoy? How could we build in more opportunities for these things?
- Which of my teenager's strengths and abilities can I encourage?
- What do they really struggle with? How can I help?
- What is likely to be the next hurdle for them? How can I help?
- How are they getting on with the family and other friends?
- Having looked back and forward, what are the three 'must do's' for them in the next month or year?
- What do I think my child would wish for in the coming year?
- What would I like to see in our relationship in the coming year?

(Adapted from *Parentalk* – a parenting course produced by Care for the Family in 1999, created and co-ordinated by Wendy Bray and Steve Williams.)

NOTES

Session 2
ON THE RADAR SCREEN
Teenage Communication

INTRODUCTION TO THE SESSION

- We'll discuss the different issues involved in communicating with our teenagers.
- We'll take a look at our listening skills, and learning to read between the lines of what is said on the surface of one-word sentences!
- We'll look at the importance of the whole family spending time together, communicating at the level of feelings.

A. ON THE RIGHT WAVELENGTH

Adults and teenagers communicate in very different ways:

The way adults tend to communicate	The way teenagers tend to communicate
By using reason, logic – prefer to stick to one topic at a time.	Stream of consciousness, easily switching between topics – like surfing the net or switching TV channels.
To solve problems, get results, change behaviour.	By talking at length without necessarily looking for solutions.
By lecturing or moralising, at times getting heavy and intense.	Like to leave things open-ended; don't need to have a point; enjoy talking for its own sake.
Interrogation-style! 'Have you...?' 'Are you...?' 'Aren't you...?' etc.	Open up when least expect it and usually not to order.
Pushing to know the whole situation to learn from the details.	Less focused; more easily distracted; shorter attention span.
Generally in a hurry. Have high expectations of what can be achieved in a short amount of time.	Can't rush them. They are on their own timetable and often it's very slow!
Value listening – try not to interrupt.	Don't mind interrupting – if a thought is in their mind, it's on their lips!

(Adapted by Nicky and Sila Lee from *Almost Cool* by Tim Smith.)

Exercise:
In what ways does this chart reveal some of the communication with our teenager?

> Bible View:
>
> 'Praise be to the God and Father of our Lord Jesus Christ, the Father of compassion and the God of all comfort, who comforts us in all our troubles, so that we can comfort those in any trouble with the comfort we ourselves have received from God.' (2 Corinthians 1:3–4)
>
> God can reassure and encourage us on any communication issues with our teenagers, and we too can reassure them. God's comfort communicates across every barrier.

B. PICKING UP THE SIGNALS

'Parents of teenagers face a difficult dilemma: how to help when help is resented, how to guide when guidance is rejected, how to communicate when attention is taken as attack.' (Haim Ginott)

1. Showing interest in their world

Learn the details of their lives. Prove to them that their world is important to you.

Exercise:
• *What programmes, music, magazines, etc., influence your teenager?*

• *Do you know anything about them?*

- *Have you dismissed or criticised their choices in any way?*

2. Adjusting to their timing

- Respond to the moment
- Create the atmosphere

Exercise:
- *When have you found you've had your best conversations with your teenagers?*

- *How were these conversations initiated?*

Turn and share with the person next to you.

3. Listening to their concerns

- Read the signs
- Look beneath the surface

  'The more a child becomes aware of a parent's willingness to listen, the more a parent will begin to hear.' (*Parentalk*)

How to listen *badly*! (Adapted from *Parentalk*)

- Switch off regularly when you think you know what your teenager is going to say.
- When you hear a phrase that makes you angry, like 'everyone else is

going' or 'everyone else is allowed', explode and cut across them before they've finished.

- Make sure you always look distracted and glassy-eyed when your teenager's talking, then they can be sure you haven't really heard them.
- Always concentrate on the subject being talked about rather than the person speaking, then you're sure to miss all the non-verbal clues about how they feel.

I'm sure we all recognise something of ourselves in this list!

Exercise:
Think of one occasion recently when you've either listened well or listened badly.

- *If it was a positive experience, what helped you to listen?*

- *If it was a negative experience, what hindered you?*

- *Why do you think you were unable to hear or to pick up the signals?*

After filling in the answers, turn to your spouse or the person next to you and share your experiences for just a couple of minutes.

4. Responding to their issues

The most common things that stop us from responding well to our teenagers are often our own anxieties, fears, anger and time pressures.

Examples:
James: 'Why are you treating me like a child?'
Parent: 'Because you behave like a child. . .'

Clare: 'I don't care.'
Parent: 'No, you never think of anybody but yourself.'

Pete: 'My mates all say pot is harmless.'
Parent: 'Well, they're just stupid. . .'

Sarah: 'I've nobody to go to the disco with.'
Parent: 'Maybe it's just as well. You can save some money.'

Exercise (in small groups):
Ask each other:

• *What do you think the parents are failing to hear in these different scenarios? What do you think is going on under the surface?*

• *What do you think will be the result of interactions like these between parent and teenager?*

• *How do you think the teenagers feel in these scenarios?*

• *In each case, what could the parent say instead?*

Bible View:

'Take note of this: Everyone should be quick to listen, slow to speak and slow to become angry.' (James 1:19)

Some have said that God gave us two ears and only one mouth because it takes twice as much effort to listen as to speak! Certainly we all need the reminder to be quick to do the first and slow to do the second. The first expresses sympathy, while the second tends merely to express opinions.

C. TUNING IN TOGETHER

What can the family offer your children through their teenage years? Here are four ingredients to think about:

1. Shared identity

- Is your teenager proud to belong to your family?
- Is your family a safe place for them?

2. Shared values

- Does your teenager know what you believe?
- Do you help them to think through their ideas and beliefs?

Exercise:
Write down your family's top three values. Under each put down how your teenager would catch that value from you, and how you are working it out in your family life. After filling in the answers, turn and share with the person next to you.

- *What are your family's top three values?*

- *How have you communicated them and passed them on to your teenagers?*

Value no. 1
How caught?

How worked out?

Value no. 2
How caught?

How worked out?

Value no. 3
How caught?

How worked out?

> Bible View:
>
> 'Love the Lord your God with all your heart and with all your soul and with all your strength. These commandments are to be upon your hearts. Impress them on your children. Talk about them when you sit at home and when you walk along the road, when you lie down and when you get up.' (Deuteronomy 6:5–7)
>
> The values our teenagers pick up from us will be those they see we are committed to, concerned for, talk about and model in our own lives.

'Values are something to do *with* our teenagers, not *to* our teenagers!' (Tim Smith)

3. Shared experiences

- Does your teenager enjoy being part of the family?
- Can you see relationships in the family deepening?

4. Shared feelings

- Does your teenager feel free to express his/her views?
- Is your teenager willing to listen to other members of the family?

DISCUSSION GROUPS

Scenarios

1. From being a chatty 12-year-old, my 14-year-old son is now completely monosyllabic. He seems moody and unhappy, and I'm worried that he's hiding something from me. How can I get him to communicate?

2. My two teenage daughters are constantly fighting – it is nearly always about clothes that they've borrowed from each other. They are both very different and don't seem to have anything in common, which just widens the gulf between them. How can I help them to get on with each other?

3. My daughter always has to have the last word and this causes real friction between us. What can I do?

Follow-up questions

1. How could you encourage your family to meet together regularly?

2. Do your teenagers have a strong sense of family identity?

3. Is there any particular person in your family who is more vulnerable or isolated at the moment?

4. How have you encouraged members of your family to express their feelings and emotions?

TAKING IT FURTHER

If you don't do it already, suggest having a regular family meal together once a week. Begin this week.

Try out one of the suggestions on how to express your feelings, e.g. 'mad, bad, sad or glad' or 'high/low'. What was the response?

NOTES

Session 3
BUILT TO LAST
Teenage Character

INTRODUCTION TO THE SESSION

- We're going to look at adolescent development and how teenagers think about themselves.
- We'll think about how they feel secure and loved by us.
- We'll ask how we can encourage them in their faith.

A. THE FOUNDATION OF INNER STRENGTH

Building self-esteem

Children learn what they live

If. . .

If a child lives with criticism . . .	he learns to condemn.
If a child lives with hostility . . .	he learns to fight.
If a child lives with ridicule . . .	he learns to be shy.
If a child lives with shame . . .	he learns to feel guilty.
If a child lives with tolerance . . .	he learns to be patient.
If a child lives with encouragement . . .	he learns confidence.
If a child lives with praise . . .	he learns to appreciate.
If a child lives with fairness . . .	he learns justice.
If a child lives with security . . .	he learns to have faith.
If a child lives with approval . . .	he learns to like himself.

If a child lives with acceptance and friendship . . .

. . .he learns to find love in the world.

Dorothy Low Nolte

Bible View:

'We were gentle among you, like a mother caring for her little children.'
'We dealt with each of you as a father deals with his own children, encouraging, comforting and urging you to live lives worthy of God, who calls you into his kingdom and glory.' (1 Thessalonians 2:7,11–12)

Generous care, encouraging praise, supportive comfort and urging affirmation – these have always been the true qualities of parenthood, and they are needed more than ever in the teenage years.

Exercise:
- *Remind yourselves of all the good qualities in your teenager.*

- *How could you let your teenager know about the good things you see in them?*

'Your teenager needs constant reassurance that they're special.' (Steve Chalke, *The Parentalk Guide to the Teenage Years*)

Adolescence

A time of enormous change:

1. Physical changes.
2. Mental and emotional changes.
3. Social changes.
4. Sexual changes.

These changes can cause great insecurity and confusion.

Our teenagers constantly question themselves:

- What am I really like?
- How do I come across to others?
- What do other boys/girls think of me?
- Am I really as ugly as I think I am?
- Will anyone ever love me?

Their answers to these questions will be mostly negative unless they have developed a healthy self-esteem. Helping our teenagers to think of themselves in a right and positive way will be one of the greatest gifts we can give them as they face the outside world.

Good self-esteem is the secret ingredient that helps get many young people through adolescence relatively unscathed. It's probably one of the strongest weapons we can give our teenagers to cope with pressure from peers, enabling them to resist doing or achieving things simply to be liked by others.

Others will judge our teenagers on what they do or what they look like. We, as parents, must be the exception to that rule.

Exercise:
- *When do we find it most difficult to love our teenager?*

- *What matters most to us? Try to answer as honestly as you can, giving these statements a grade from 1 to 5 (1 = important, 5 = not important).*
  - *What he/she looks like.*
  - *Exam results.*
  - *Good manners.*
  - *Sporting achievements.*
  - *Job prospects.*
  - *Not smoking.*
  - *Not taking drugs.*
  - *Keeping a faith.*

You can probably add a few of your own below!

'Unconditional love is loving a child no matter what we expect him to be, and most difficult, no matter how he acts.' (Ross Campbell, *How to Really Love Your Teenager*)

Signs of a young person with good self-esteem

They will tend to:

- take on new experiences willingly
- be open to making new friends
- be happy not always to be the centre of attention
- be generous with praise of other people's achievements
- treat others with consideration
- not be too judgemental
- be prepared to admit their mistakes
- be able to take positive criticism

Signs of a young person with low self-esteem

They will tend to:

- shy away from new experiences
- be very protective of existing friends and suspicious of new ones
- be in constant need of reassurance
- be too competitive in areas where they feel confident
- blame others for their mistakes
- find assurance in the faults of others
- get angry and defensive when criticised
- feel they have to constantly do things to make others like them, e.g. give presents, lend things, clown around or do favours

Exercise:
Your teenager is probably a mixture of these two lists, but which one best describes him/her?

- *Which of these different qualities can we already see developing in our teenager?*

- *Which of these qualities need special encouragement?*

After answering the questions, turn and share with the person next to you.

Your teenager's self-esteem will grow when you praise them.

Motto for parents:
'Catch your teenager doing something right – and praise them for it!'

Praise should be . . .

1. Specific not general.
2. Genuine not patronising.
3. About effort as much as achievement.
4. Straightforward not comparing.
5. Unconditional, no strings attached.
6. About gifts not bribes.
7. Unqualified not half-hearted.

Exercise:
- *Which of these are you prone to get wrong?*

- *In what ways and on what occasions have you most effectively praised your teenager?*

After answering the questions, turn and share with the person next to you.

B. THE BUILDING MATERIALS

Filling the emotional tank

'A teenager is the most vulnerable person in society, and his deepest need is love.' (Ross Campbell)

Bible View:

'The only thing that counts is faith expressing itself through love.'
'The entire law is summed up in a single command: "Love your neighbour as yourself".'
'Carry each other's burdens, and in this way you will fulfil the law of Christ.'
(Galatians 5:6,14; 6:2)

To discover the appropriate expression of love for each individual is the most caring thing we can do for them.

The five love languages

1. Words
2. Time
3. Affection
4. Presents
5. Actions

(Adapted from Gary Chapman, *Five Love Languages*)

Discovering our teenagers' primary love language

Exercise:
Try to rank the five ways of expressing love in order of priority for each of your teenagers.

Name ....   **Name** ....

1.   1.

2.   2.

3.   3.

4.   4.

5.   5.

Name ....   **Name** ....

1.   1.

2.   2.

3.   3.

4.   4.

5.   5.

C. A SECURE STRUCTURE

Keeping God at the centre

Bible View:

'Then we will no longer be infants, tossed back and forth by the waves, and blown here and there by every wind of teaching and by the cunning and craftiness of men in their deceitful scheming. Instead, speaking the truth in love, we will in all things grow up into him who is the Head, that is, Christ.' (Ephesians 4:14–15)

The teenage years are ones of growth in every way: physically, mentally, socially – and there is no reason why they should not also be tremendous times of growth in character and spiritual maturity, towards stability and independence.

How can you help your teenager continue to grow in their Christian faith? What role can you expect to play in these teenage years?

Here are a few suggestions:

1. Learn to let go.
2. Pray hard for them!
3. Don't underestimate the indirect influence you can still have on them.
4. Be careful about any relocation during their teenage years.
5. Put good Christian material around the house.
6. Look out for good holiday/work/gap-year experiences.
7. Always remain open for conversation.

DISCUSSION GROUPS

Scenarios

1. My 15-year-old daughter really seems to dislike her appearance. She's always making comments about how big her nose is or how fat her thighs are. Nothing I say seems to make any impact. How can I help her?

2. My 14-year-old son has always been mediocre at sport, but he's desperate to be accepted by the sporty crowd in his year. I can see that they don't really include him, but he's now given up on his few old friends to try to be part of this new group. I don't want him to be left with no friends at all. What should I do?

3. My 16-year-old son is struggling with the exam workload. He won't take advice and seems to have almost given up. My husband, who used to be a teacher, has tried to help him, but it always ends in raised voices and slammed doors. What should we do?

Follow-up questions

1. Do you relate personally to the suggestion that certain acts make you feel more loved than others?

2. Do you agree on what your teenager's primary love languages are?

3. How are you planning to feed those?

TAKING IT FURTHER

1. Try out your teenagers' top love language on them this week. What impact did it have?

2. Try praising your teenagers for something, however small, every day this week. What impact did it have?

NOTES

Session 4
BOUNDARIES AND BATTLEFIELDS
Teenage Tensions

INTRODUCTION TO THE SESSION

- We'll think through some of the battles that arise during these years, and consider setting positive, healthy boundaries for our teenagers.
- We'll outline some of the areas of conflict, and give some guidelines on how to face issues together, distinguishing important ones from unimportant ones.
- We'll recognise the ongoing pressure from their contemporaries.

A. TO BOLDLY GO

Exploring the limits

1. Set boundaries

Seen on a teenager's badge: 'I'm bored – forbid me to do something.'

> Bible View:
>
> 'Children, obey your parents in the Lord . . . Honour your father and mother.'
> 'Fathers, do not exasperate your children; instead, bring them up in the training and instruction of the Lord.' (Ephesians 6:1, 4)
>
> Growing up involves moving from 'obey your parents' (for young children) to still 'honour your father and mother' (for children of all ages!). But this assumes the right to be obeyed ('in the Lord'), and continually honoured. Parents who provoke their children with arbitrary demands are the opposite of those who nurture them by good example with consistent boundaries.

We, as parents, should be moving from a place of parental control to one of parental trust.

'As hard as it is, our role must move from controller to consultant. What do consultants do? They ask questions, offer opinions, share experiences, present options and forecast outcomes. Ultimately, however, they step back and allow the client to make decisions. Consultants understand what they can and cannot do for their clients, and as a result the client owns the process as well as the results.' (Daniel Hahn)

2. Encourage responsibility

Aim to help them to take responsibility for their actions – to 'own' their choices.

Exercise:

Which of the following tasks have you handed over or could you hand over to your teenagers?

- *Preparing meals.*
- *Washing/ironing clothes.*
- *Helping with a younger sibling.*
- *Getting themselves to school on time.*
- *Locking doors at night.*
- *Cleaning the bathroom.*
- *Settling their own arguments.*
- *Making decisions about their routines.*

3. Be ready to say 'no'

We need a united front. We need to be prepared to say 'no':

- to the teenage 'naggers'
- to the teenager who pushes for an immediate answer
- to the teenager who insists that everyone else's parent says it's OK

4. Work out consequences

What do we do when they cross over the boundaries? Ask yourself: Did they cross the boundary:

- without realising?
- by an error?
- through immaturity?
- for attention-seeking?
- in defiance?

All these crossings need different handling, but you first need to be reasonably sure which one you're dealing with!

Exercise:
- *Think of one incident recently when your teenager crossed a boundary. Which of the five boundary crossings was made?*

- *Do you think that you assessed the situation correctly at the time – or do you see it rather differently now?*

After answering the questions, turn and share with the person next to you.

B. EMPIRE WARS

Choosing our battles

When drawing up the battle plans:

1. Always ask yourself: Is it worth the fight?

Keep the guns for the big issues.

> Bible View:
> 'My son, do not forget my teaching, but keep my commands in your heart, for they will prolong your life many years and bring you prosperity.'
> 'Discipline your son, for in that there is hope; do not be a willing party to his death.'
> 'Train a child in the way he should go, and when he is old he will not turn from it.'
> (Proverbs 3:1–2; 19:18; 22:6)
>
> The battles worth fighting are the ones that may bring lifelong benefit or avert life-long harm.

Generally, the things that annoy parents of teenagers the most are:

- staying up (or staying out) late at night
- not getting up in the morning
- moaning about or ignoring your requests for help
- spending hours on their mobiles/the internet/TV
- not doing homework
- loud music
- being rude/unkind to siblings
- (add your own)

Exercise (on your own):
Which of the above things about your teenager's behaviour make you angry again and again? (Put a star against the top three.)

Does all this sound familiar? Be assured that you are not alone!

2. Check yourself before you check them

Bible View:

'First take the plank out of your own eye, and then you will see clearly to remove the speck from your brother's eye.' (Matthew 7:5)

Three of our most common problems are:

- depression
- fatigue
- anxiety

Exercise in pairs:
- *Are you or have you been susceptible to any of these in particular?*

- *What effects does depression, fatigue or anxiety have on you?*

- *How does your teenager perceive this condition?*

3. Learn how to face conflict; it isn't always a bad thing!

> Bible View:
>
> 'Better is open rebuke than hidden love.'(Proverbs 27:5)
>
> We are often tempted to avoid confrontation in the name of a misjudged love. But that can lead to denial, pretending we haven't seen something that needs to be dealt with; or double standards, reacting inconsistently.

Take steps to handle your anger and your teenager's.

'Self-control is something we most need when we least want it!' (Rob Parsons)

Three things to watch:

- Don't overreact.
- Don't jump to conclusions.
- Don't be hurtful.

(Adapted from Tim Smith, *Almost Cool*)

Exercise:

- *Think of an incident recently when you attacked your teenager's character rather than the issue.*

- *How could you have spoken more helpfully?*

Turn and share with the person next to you.

4. Shouting is just louder, not necessarily more effective!

Bible View:

'Do not let any unwholesome talk come out of your mouths, but only what is helpful for building others up.' (Ephesians 4:29)
'The tongue also is a fire.'(James 3:6)

Fires can get out of control, and then they do damage. So too can a habit of reacting with louder and louder shouts or threats.

Necessary shouting:
- *'Stop!'*
  (Tone implies instant obedience for their safety.)
- *'Oi, come here!'*
  (Useful for large gardens, loft extensions and teenagers with headphones on.)

Unnecessary shouting:

- *'Let's get some action around here'*

(Demands instant obedience, but denies any prior explanation or warnings.)
- *'Oh please come on'*
  (The wearied whine – otherwise known as nagging.)
- *'What the heck'*
  (I've been shouting all day so I may as well shout some more!)
- *'I don't deserve this kind of treatment'*
  (The adult version of a tantrum!)

(Adapted from *Parentalk*)

5. Remember how important it is to say sorry and move on

Bible View:

'Bear with each other and forgive whatever grievances you may have against one another. Forgive as the Lord forgave you.'
'Fathers do not embitter your children, or they will become discouraged.'
(Colossians 3:13, 21)

Saying sorry and forgiving must work in both directions in all human relationships. In parent–teenager relationships it is the key to stemming a growing tide of resentments.

Exercise:
- *When was the last time you apologised – or should have apologised – to your teenager?*

C. AN ARMY OF CLONES

Coping with peer pressure

'At the heart of each of us is a need to belong.' (Paul Tripp)

Bible View:

'In Christ we who are many form one body, and each member belongs to all the others.' (Romans 12:5)

The desire to belong to a social group is part of the way we are wired. That instinct for community can be fulfilled in many ways, but the deepest and most satisfying way will feed our spiritual as well as our social dimension.

Your teenager will increasingly make their own choices about who they see and what they do.

Keep in touch with how your teenager is feeling about themselves and about their friends.

Exercise:
Do you know:

• *Where your teenager finds the most pressure – at school, youth group, in the sports team, on the street?*

• *Where your child comes in the pecking order?*

- *Whether they feel that they have to work hard to be accepted among their peers?*

Exercise:
Look at the way your teenager introduces their friends to you.

- *How do they behave with them when you are around? Are they embarrassed and evasive?*

- *Is there space somewhere in the home for them to hang out together?*

- *Do they feel you like or dislike their friends? Why? How much do you see of them?*

DISCUSSION GROUPS

Scenarios

1. My teenagers have to be at school by 8.30 am. They are always leaving things until the last minute, and there is usually a hiatus when something goes missing. They invariably end up asking me for a lift as they've missed the bus and will get a late mark. What can I do to organise our mornings better?

2. I've tried to encourage my 14-year-old son to bring friends home with him. He won't. I really want to meet his friends and know more about who he's hanging out with. How can I make this happen?

3. During a heated discussion with our teenage daughter, my husband told her that she couldn't go to a party that I know she'd been looking forward to for weeks. I feel this was over-hasty, but I don't want to undermine his authority. How should we move forward?

Follow-up questions:

1. How can you help your teenagers resist negative peer pressure?

2. How can you prevent the same old things causing friction in the home time and time again?

TAKING IT FURTHER

Let's surprise our teenagers this week:

1. Think of one bit of their behaviour that upsets you regularly, and plan to do the opposite to what you normally do.

2. Begin by making a small change rather than a major one – the more specific the better. Set yourself realistic goals.

Examples:
- You're always getting drawn into and 'wound up' by the petty squabbles between two of your children, so decide instead to leave them to sort things out themselves.

- You've got into a habit of shouting, so say to yourself, 'I'll only yell at them five times today instead of ten!'
- You find yourself constantly criticising the way they dress, so instead of making negative comments, compliment them on one thing.

NOTES

Session 5
SECURITY, SEX AND SUBSTANCES
Teenage Issues

INTRODUCTION TO THE SESSION

- We'll tackle some of the big issues to help teenagers face the world in which they are emerging as adults. We'll think through some of the various disorders, physical and mental, and signs to watch out for.
- We'll try to facilitate good, open conversations about their relationships, and the whirlwind of emotions surrounding these.
- We'll explore the whole area of substance abuse, dependence and addiction.

A. HEALTH ISSUES

Bible View:

'Do you not know that your body is a temple of the Holy Spirit, who is in you, whom you have received from God? You are not your own; you were bought at a price. Therefore honour God with your body.' (1 Corinthians 6:19–20)

There is a right ownership of responsibility for our bodies, but it is not an absolute self-determination. It is more a delegated responsibility – we are to look after our bodies precisely because they are not ours to do with as we like.

Eating disorders

'90% of teenage girls say that they hate their body.' (Dr Kate Middleton, Anorexia & Bulimia Care)

Recent studies reveal that as many as a quarter of young teenage girls may have some kind of eating disorder, and that by the age of 13 around two-thirds of girls have already been on a diet.

Warning signs

- Obsession – reading books/articles on dieting, checking food labels for fat/calorie content.
- Control – developing a strict list of 'forbidden' foods.
- Isolation – eating alone or out of sight.
- Deception – saying they've eaten when offered a meal.
- Neurosis – complaining of feeling 'bloated'.
- Secrecy – finding hidden food or stashes of food wrappers.
- Excessive behaviour – frequent exercising.
- Binge-eating – food inexplicably disappearing from the kitchen.

What to do as a parent

- Get alongside – ask them what would be helpful.

- Show them you want to understand their struggle.
- Discover if there are particular pressures on them.
- Help them to make their own choices.
- Give affirmation without overwhelming them.
- Work together – read books/look at websites.

What not to do as a parent

- Don't say or do nothing – it implies you're frightened or don't care.
- Don't let your shock or fear show more than your concern.
- Don't expect them to pull themselves together and eat normally.
- Don't try to control their eating habits.
- Don't condemn or judge them.
- Don't expose them.

B. LSD – LOVE, SEX AND DATING

Our teenagers live in a world where they are constantly bombarded by other people's views on sex. There are pressures on them:

- from within themselves
- from outside themselves

  – their peers
  – society

'There's a battle going on for our teenagers' minds – if you're not influencing them, you're about the only person in their lives who isn't!' (Steve Chalke)

Bible View:

'It is God's will that you should be sanctified: that you should avoid sexual immorality; that each of you should learn to control his own body in a way that is holy and honourable.' (1 Thessalonians 4:3–4)

'Sexual immorality' is every form of sexual relationship outside of the lifelong commitment of marriage. Treating other people honourably is a control that has to be learned.

How can we best communicate our values and beliefs? Moralising doesn't work. Instead:

- Ask them questions.
- Give them opportunities to talk.
- Allow them to express their opinions.
- Help them to set their own guidelines.

You might ask them:

- 'What advice would you give your younger brother or sister before going out on their first date?'
- 'How would you like to be treated on a date?'
- 'How would you answer if he said that you don't really love him if you don't want to have sex?'
- 'What do your friends say about sex?'

'Don't Panic' list:

- Don't live in denial.
- Don't bring too much attention to the changes.
- Don't show anxiety or foreboding.
- Don't deny their feelings – if she feels you only want the 'happy child', she may only try to connect with you when she's happy.
- Don't leave them to work out their own sexual standards and goals.
- Don't be taken unawares – e.g. as they're going out the door for their first teenage party, you desperately summarise in two minutes the two-hour talk you should have had months before!

Exercise in pairs:
• *What are some of the things making you panic as your teenager hits puberty?*

We can't make their choices for them, but we can help their choices to be informed and responsible.

The slow 'drip-feed' method is more effective than the one 'Big Talk'! (Nicky and Sila Lee)

Work out what you would say on:

• changes in body size and shape
• changes in hair, voice, skin, body odour
• sexual organs
• masturbation
• virginity
• pornography
• sexual attraction
• flirting/kissing/heavy petting
• the dangers of casual sex – physical and emotional

Keep the channels of communication open.

• Take the initiative – don't just wait for questions.
• Pick up on natural opportunities.
• Don't get too heavy or intense.

Keep talking

Questions you might ask your teenager:

1. Why do you think TV and films rarely show sex that isn't perfect?

2. How can you tell the difference between lust and love? How do you know when 'this is the one'?

3. What limits would you set in a relationship and why? How would you get over the embarrassment of talking about your limits with a boy or girlfriend?

4. Why do you think people ignore the dangers of casual sex?

5. What do you think makes marriage different from living together?

6. What makes a good relationship? What makes a bad one? What do you look for in a boy or girlfriend?

7. Do you think it's good to wait until you get married to have sex, or not? Why?

8. Do you think it's true that people's first experience of sex makes a big impression?

Exercise:
- *What have you discovered with your own teenagers that has been particularly effective in starting good conversations?*

- *What have you discovered that has been particularly ineffective?*

After answering the questions, turn and share with the person next to you.

- Many teenagers are confused by the different messages.

- Many are missing out on the vital friendship stage.
- Many see sex as an escape from reality into 'instant intimacy'.

We can *help* our teenagers make good sexual choices, but we can't make their choices for them.

C. SAD – SMOKING, ALCOHOL AND DRUGS

'My dad said: "You've never seen any drugs, have you?"

'I knew that he just wanted me to say "No, Dad", because then he'd feel safe and as if he had nothing to worry about. He likes everything to be cosy and manageable.

'Truth is, loads of kids in my school take them and I could get him anything he wants, so I told him so. He yelled at me then as if I was already facing death as an addict.

'I'm not, I've got too much sense. He didn't see that just knowing where to get it doesn't mean you are. He couldn't see that he should be glad that I've kept on the right side of it all and learnt how to deal with the pressure. He just gave me a whole load of don'ts and a rambling lecture. To be honest, most of what he said was so out-of-date and so incorrect anyway it wouldn't have helped a bit.' (Dave, aged 16. Taken from Rob Parsons, *What Every Kid Wished Their Parents Knew*)

Reasons why teenagers use drugs and alcohol

1. It makes them feel they belong
   – takes away inhibitions.
2. It's fun
   – an easy source of pleasure.
3. It's easy to obtain them
   – 'You can get them anytime, anywhere'.
4. It's the 'in' thing to do
   – it's just part of a night out.

5. It fills the emptiness
   – feelings of worthlessness and loneliness disappear.
6. It offers relief from internal pressures
   – gives an immediate 'high'.
7. It's 'cool' to take risks
   – to rebel or shock.

Exercise:
Look at the reasons above why teenagers take drugs.

• *Do you think your teenager may be feeling any of these right now?*

Turn and share with the person next to you.

Drugs are not a problem to young people – they are the answers to the problems of life.

'The reason young people take drugs is because they work.' (Paul Francis)

Just to say 'no' to our teenagers – 'Don't take drugs whatever you do' – is ineffective. They need to understand 'why'. They need life-skills to help them make good choices.

Eight tips on talking with your teenagers about drugs and alcohol

1. Ask questions – they probably know more than you think!
2. Listen carefully to what they have to say – be willing to hear something new.
3. Encourage them to talk about their feelings, not just their experiences.
4. Try not to resort to half-informed threats out of fear, e.g. 'Ecstasy kills'.

5. Talk with them about making choices – encourage them to have their own opinions.
6. Think about the messages and attitudes you are passing on to your teenagers.
7. Don't be afraid of creating rules and boundaries, particularly about what happens in your own home.
8. Understand that sometimes teenagers just like to be contrary.

Exercise:

• *Have you talked with your teenagers about drugs?*

• *How have they responded?*

• *What have you learned?*

Turn and share with the person next to you.

What if we think our teenager is taking drugs?

Look for emotional changes in your teenager's behaviour that are out of the ordinary:

• Stimulants (such as Ecstasy, poppers, speed or cocaine) excite the user. So look for significant change in sleeping patterns; bursts of energy and then periods where they seem overtired for no apparent reason.
• Hallucinogens (such as cannabis, ketamine or magic mushrooms) heighten experiences in the short term – music becomes enhanced,

jokes are funnier, emotions more overwhelming; but in the long term these drugs will make the user paranoid and moody.

- Depressants (such as gases, glues and aerosols) slow down the heart rate, often making the user sleepy – possibly causing them to have slurred speech. There is a loss of inhibitions and a numbing of the emotions.

Beware – these signs are often difficult to separate from normal teenage behaviour! Physical signs can be more obvious:

- Eating habits become very erratic.
- Their appearance changes.
- They become more secretive.
- They lose interest in schoolwork or hobbies.
- Money goes missing from your purse.

Most parents panic and become very emotional if they suspect their child is using drugs. Instead:

- Try not to accuse your teenager – this will only start a row, and if you're wrong, you will damage your relationship.
- Try not to discuss things while they are under the influence of drugs or alcohol. Choose a calmer moment.
- Try not to get angry or threaten with punishment.
- Try to let them make their own choices and to learn through the consequences.
- Try not to give up.

Bible View:

'Do not join those who drink too much . . . drowsiness clothes them in rags.' (Proverbs 23:20–21)
'Be very careful, then, how you live – not as unwise but as wise . . . Do not get drunk on wine, which leads to debauchery. Instead, be filled with the Spirit.' (Ephesians 5:15,18)

Alcohol in moderation, like other drugs that are part of the creation, is not condemned in the Bible – it is their misuse, or excessive use, or inappropriate use we are warned to be careful about.

Drinking and smoking

'Alcohol and cigarettes are gateway drugs. Drinking is a far bigger problem for teenagers today than illegal drug-taking. Alcohol abuse kills more people than all the other drugs put together.' (Paul Francis)

Alcohol is part of most recreational activity. We need to help our teenagers to handle it carefully:

- Introduce them to alcohol, usually beer or wine, at home over a meal – take away the 'mystery' factor.
- Help them to learn not to drink it too quickly, to treat it with respect – it's not Coca-Cola.
- When your teenager starts going to parties, encourage them to stick to lower-strength brands, or to drink 'long drinks'.
- Show them that even a seemingly innocent 'alcopop' contains a double measure of spirits.
- Encourage them to have something to eat before they go out – not to drink on an empty stomach.
- Tell them to look out for each other and to notice if someone has had too much to drink.

Think ahead before you hold a party at home:

- Agree that you will be around or close at hand.
- Remove temptations such as your own stock of drink (especially spirits).
- Have plenty of starchy food available – bread, rice and pasta, for example.

- Work out an end-time to the party, and discuss with your teenager how that will happen.
- Warn the neighbours!

DISCUSSION GROUPS

Scenarios

1. I do a school run with a group of my son's school friends a couple of times a week. My 13-year-old son has been openly talking with them about 'dating and dumping' girls. There is a lot of joking and boasting, and I realise most of it is sheer bravado; but I'm concerned that if I don't say anything he may assume that I approve of the way they are talking. I don't want to come across heavy-handed. What should I do?

2. My 16-year-old daughter has been going out with a boy from her school for six months. She recently told us that they have started sleeping together, and that his parents allow this to happen when she stays over at their house. We are horrified. She doesn't want us to talk to the boy's parents, but we feel that we must. We don't want to go behind her back. What should we do?

3. My 13-year-old girl has started avidly to read various teenage magazines. The problem pages in these magazines lay a lot of emphasis on how to give pleasure in a sexual relationship. I am uncomfortable with this. Is this something I should talk to my daughter about?

4. I feel differently about my son experimenting with sex from the way I feel about my daughter. Am I being inconsistent?

Follow-up questions

In what ways do you personally feel challenged:

• to review your own lifestyle choices?

• to talk more openly about any of these issues?

TAKING IT FURTHER

1. Look back at the questions in B above under 'Keep talking'. Think how you personally might answer some of these questions yourself.

2. Choose one or two of the questions and try to open up a discussion with your teenager this week.

NOTES

Session 6
CONSUMERISM, CASH AND CYBERSPACE
Teenage Pressures

INTRODUCTION TO THE SESSION

- We'll consider the tremendous pressure of advertising and the media on this very self-conscious group in society, for whom 'image' is everything, in clothes, music, electronic gizmos.
- We'll look at the stress caused by the handling, and mishandling, of money in a debt culture – and the subtle pressure of gambling.
- We'll uncover the secretive world of internet chat-rooms, virtual reality, and the increasingly absorbing problems of web-surfing, computer games and pornography – including mobile phones and texting.

A. MEDIA AND CONSUMERISM

Bible View:

'You shall not covet.' (Exodus 20:17)
'Whoever can be trusted with very little can also be trusted with much, and whoever is dishonest with very little will also be dishonest with much. So if you have
not been trustworthy in handling worldly wealth, who will trust you with true
riches? And if you have not been trustworthy with someone else's property, who
will give you property of your own?' (Luke 16:10–12)

Helping our teenagers to handle material goods, other people's things and advertising pressure is one of the most important skills we can instil in them.

Our teenagers are told that they are defined by outward signs:

You are the labels you wear,
You are the car you drive,
You are your body size/shape,
You are the level of popularity you have,
You are even the toothpaste/shampoo that you use!

As one teenager said: 'Take away my mobile phone and you take away a part of me!'

How do we keep the obsession with mobiles, gadgets, clothes and designer wear under control? All these things are a very powerful way of showing that teenagers belong to their chosen group. It's as much about belonging as about acquiring the actual items.

Ask yourself whether you have passed on your 'designer desire' to your teenager. Do you covet all the latest gadgets, high-spec cars and expensive labels?

Exercise:

• *What is most important to your teenager*

    – *quantity of clothes?*
    – *exclusive brand names/designer wear?*
    – *gadgets, e.g. mobile phone, MP3 player?*

• *Who or what influences their choices?*

• *How could you encourage them to make sensible choices without seeming mean or controlling?*

Turn and share with the person next to you.

Some suggestions

• Decide on a certain amount of money together *before* you go out shopping with them. This should help you not to be pressurised into buying things on the spur of the moment.
• Explore cut-price solutions in designer outlets.
• Show them that you want to be generous – come towards them.
• Be more open with them about the pressures on the family budget – allow them to see the bigger picture.
• Try to be positive about the choices they make. Their clothes are an expression of themselves, so compliment them – don't knock their pleasure.

B. MONEY AND DEBT

Bible View:

'Do not be a man who strikes hands in pledge or puts up security for debts; if you lack the means to pay, your very bed will be snatched from under you.'(Proverbs 22:26–27)

Debt is fast becoming one of the greatest social problems we face. It's better to warn about the dangers of debt, and give helpful training in how to handle money, before there is even the opportunity to handle a plastic card.

Work out a basic monthly allowance with them. Give them freedom to spend it as they want, and resist adding to it on demand.

A strategy for handing on responsibility

1. Train them.
2. Teach them.
3. Warn them.
4. Protect them.

Exercise:
• *What would you consider to be a reasonable monthly allowance for a 16-year-old? How are you helping your teenager to budget?*

• *When do you think is the appropriate age for teenagers to handle cash cards/credit cards/store cards?*

• *What do you think they have picked up from watching how you spend money?*

Turn and share with the person next to you.

C. GITS – GAMES, INTERNET, TEXTING AND SURFING

The internet offers many things:

• Easy accessibility.
• Continuous entertainment.
• Stimulation with no demands or commitments.
• The opportunity for anonymity.
• An escape from reality.
• A secret place where inhibitions are lowered.
• An increased sense of intimacy.

How can we as parents watch for the signs of it becoming an obsession, even an addiction, with our teenagers?

Obsessive behaviour takes the form of particular activities, and might include any or all of the following:

• Relationships – spending excessive amounts of time starting and maintaining online friendships in chat-rooms, which begin to replace real-life friends and family.
• Money – compulsively gambling online, trading online and taking part in online auctions.
• Information searching – compulsive web-surfing or database searches.
• Gaming – obsessive computer game playing, including multi-user games.
• Sex – addiction to adult chat-rooms, cyber sex or pornography on the internet.

Here are some other indicators that may help you decide if your teenager is spending too much time online:

- Preoccupation with the internet – it becomes the strongest source of satisfaction in their lives.
- Less investment in relationships with friends – it begins to take precedence over other arrangements/commitments.
- An increased emptiness, depression and irritability when not at the computer.
- A deception about the amount of time spent online.
- Lack of sleep through long and often late hours on the computer.
- Declining school results and a lack of interest in other activities.
- A denial of the seriousness of the problem.

Here are some suggestions as you try to establish healthy boundaries:

- Try to avoid computers in bedrooms – move the computer into a shared family room.
- Try to find out how much time they really are spending online. You can do this without them realising, if you're careful!
- Try to work out some ground rules. Don't ban the internet – that will only make them mad! Instead, work out:
  - where they go online
  - an agreed 'internet time' – limiting the amount of time they spend online each day
  - an agreement on no surfing or instant messaging until they complete their homework
  - a policy to limit access to chat-rooms

- Try talking to them about why they're spending so much time online.
- Try encouraging them to participate in other activities, particularly physical ones. Maybe find an offline activity that links in with their online interest.

- Try speaking to their teacher, or the school's counsellor, or even seek help from your local GP.

(For more information on time-limiting tools visit: www.kids.get netwise.org/tools/timelimits – but be sure to discuss this with your teenager first.)

> **Bible View:**
>
> 'Do not love the world or anything in the world . . . the cravings of sinful man, the lust of his eyes and the boasting of what he has and does.' (1 John 2:15–16) 'Keep yourselves from idols.' (1 John 5:21)
>
> An idol is rarely a bad thing in itself, but rather a good thing in the wrong place in our longing and affection – obsessive habits, possessive ownership, compulsive use. Ultimately, idolatry is worship of the created goods of this world rather than of the good Creator, who alone can bring these things under control.

DISCUSSION GROUPS

Scenarios

1. My 14-year-old daughter seems to have no hobbies or interests at all; just a circle of friends she spends all her time with reading teenage magazines, trying out make-up and swapping clothes. The frivolity of this gets me down. What can I do to encourage more constructive use of her time?

2. My 15-year-old son is addicted to computer games. He seems to want to do nothing else and I can't bear the violence of the games he chooses. What can I do?

3. I'm worried that my 16-year-old daughter is going into chat-rooms and making contact with unknown characters. She is becoming more

withdrawn and secretive, turning off the computer when I enter the room. I have also just realised how late she is staying online at night. She dismisses my attempts to talk to her about this and says I'm being paranoid. What should I do?

Follow-up questions

1. Should we pay our teenagers to baby-sit for their younger siblings?

2. Is it wrong to offer money incentives for passing exams?

TAKING IT FURTHER

What can I do to parent my teenager(s) better?

List six things that have particularly struck you while doing the course. Be as practical as you can.

1.

2.

3.

4.

5.

6.

When can I put some of these into effect?

Commit yourself to an action plan to work on these things in the weeks ahead.

NOTES

Recommended Books

Biddulph, Steve, *Raising Boys*, Thorsons (HarperCollins) 1997.

Campbell, Ross, *Kids in Danger*, Chariot Victor 1995.

Campbell, Ross, *How to Really Love Your Teenager*, Authentic Media 1999.

Chalke, Steve, *The ParentTalk Guide to the Teenage Years*, Hodder & Stoughton 1999.

Chapman, Gary, *The Five Love Languages*, Northfield Publishing 2000.

Dobson, James, *Preparing for Adolescence*, Kingsway Publications 1982.

Francis, Paul, *Help Your Kids Stay Drug-free*, HarperCollins 1999.

Lee, Nicky & Sila, *The Marriage Book*, HTB Publications 2000.

Melluish, Mark & Lindsay, *Parenting Children*, Kingsway Publications 2007.

Parsons, Rob, *The Sixty-Minute Father*, Hodder & Stoughton 1995.

Parsons, Rob, *The Sixty-Minute Mother*, Hodder & Stoughton 2000.

Parsons, Rob, *Teenagers-What Every Parent Has to Know*, Hodder & Stoughton 2007.

Parsons, Rob and Lloyd, *What Every Kid Wished Their Parents Knew*, Hodder & Stoughton 1999.

Quinn, Michael & Terri, *What Can the Parent of a Teenager Do?*, Family Caring Trust 1988.

Smith, Tim, A*lmost Cool*, Moody Press 1999.

Tripp, Paul David, *Age of Opportunity*, P & R Publishing 2001.

Acknowledgements

We are very grateful indeed to the following people as we've worked on this course:

Mark & Lindsay Melluish – for entrusting to us the sequel of their 'Family Time – Parenting Children' course, it's been such a privilege working with them.

Nicky and Sila Lee – who have pioneered marriage and family courses over the years, and who have inspired us in writing this course.

Rob Parsons – for his wonderful illustrations and deep insights into all aspects of family life.

To many members of our own congregation at St Mark's who have helped and encouraged us with this material over the last few years.

And particularly to our three children – Emily, Julia and Max – who have bravely allowed their stories to be used, and who have vetted their transmission along the way!